CLUB PENGUIN CHARACTERS

ROCKHOPPER

Rockhopper is a pirate captain originally from Club Penguin who calls the sea his home. He isn't happy unless he's braving the ocean, looking for adventure. His favourite way to unwind at the end of a busy day is drawing maps, while enjoying a cream soda.

His best friend is his red puffle, Yarr, who is also the first mate of Rockhopper's ship, the Migrator. Rockhopper built the Migrator with his own bare flippers. Rockhopper's favourite sayings include "Ahoy!" and "Avast".

And when he isn't sailing, he likes counting treasure, dancing jigs and giving penguins a tour of his ship.

AUNT ARCTIC

Keeping everyone up-to-date with the weekly news, Aunt Arctic reports and edits the Club Penguin Times. She has her own column that any penguin can write in to, called "Ask Aunt Arctic", so she's great at giving lots of advice.

Aunt Arctic is also something of a Club Penguin historian and loves keeping up on all the goings-on, which is why she's perfect for giving tips and secrets. And if she doesn't have the answer, she knows how to find out! Aunt Arctic never misses a party and even organized the Easter Scavenger Hunt in 2007.

There are lots of things that make Aunt Arctic smile, like penguins who work together and help each other out, collecting things, researching island history and decorating her igloo in different themes.

CLUB PENGUIN CHARACTERS

GARY THE GADGET GUY

Gary the Gadget Guy is Club Penguin's resident inventor and scientist. He also has a secret identity when he works for the Penguin Secret Agency. Known as "G," Gary helps secret agents with missions and equips them with the latest spy gear. As an inventor, Gary comes to the rescue with his inventions whenever there's an emergency.

SENSEI

Sensei can be found in the Dojo. A master of the game Card-Jitsu and Card-Jitsu Fire, Sensei is both powerful and wise. The name "Sensei" means "teacher" and he can help penguins train to become ninjas. Sensei will play Card-Jitsu with anyone... but only masters can defeat him.

CADENCE

Cadence is a talented DJ, musician, artist, dancer and choreographer –all rolled into one! Otherwise known as "DJ K Dance", she is enthusiastic, confident and great at giving advice. Grooving to her own beat, Cadence is passionate about dancing and listening to music.

She throws fabulous parties and also loves to make everyone laugh with her razor-sharp wit! Head to the Night Club and join in all the fun!

THE PUFFLES

Puffles make great pets and you can keep them forever!
Read the puffle profiles below to decide which ones suit you.

BLUE PUFFLE

Attitude: Mild-tempered, content and loyal
Favourite toy: Ball
Special features: Loyal, easy to take care of

RED PUFFLE

Attitude: Adventurous and enthusiastic
Favourite toys: Bowling pins and cannon
Special feature: Originally from Rockhopper Island

BLACK PUFFLE (MEMBERS ONLY)

Attitude: Strong and silent type
Favourite toy: Skateboard
Special feature: Sometimes very energetic

PINK PUFFLE (MEMBERS ONLY)

Attitude: Active and cheery
Favourite toys: Skipping rope and trampoline
Special feature: Loves to exercise

YELLOW PUFFLE (MEMBERS ONLY)

Attitude: Artistic and spontaneous
Favourite toys: Paintbrush and easel
Special features: Very creative and a dreamer

GREEN PUFFLE (MEMBERS ONLY)

Attitude: Energetic and playful
Favourite toys: Unicycle and propeller cap
Special feature: Likes to clown around

PURPLE PUFFLE (MEMBERS ONLY)

Attitude: A bit of a diva
Favourite toys: Bubble wand and disco ball
Special feature: Loves to dance

WHITE PUFFLE (MEMBERS ONLY)

Attitude: gentle, strong
Favourite toy: skate
Special feature: can turn anything to ice with a breath

ORANGE PUFFLE (MEMBERS ONLY)

Attitude: zany, curious
Favourite toy: box, wagon
Special feature: sleeps very deeply

ROCKHOPPER'S TREASURE HUNT

Rockhopper and his first mate, Yarr, are happiest when they are searching for treasure. Can you help them through the maze and lead them to the treasure chest?

START

PENGUIN, PLACE, OR THING?

Can You Guess Who (or What) I Am?

1 I am not always on Club Penguin.

2 To see me when I am near, you need to go to a high place.

3 I am always searching for something.

4 My best friend always travels with me.

5 Club Penguin is not the only island I visit.

6 When I am around, many penguins want to meet me.

7 My favourite beverage is cream soda.

8 I love the sea.

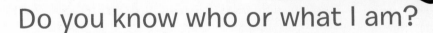

Do you know who or what I am?

_____

LET'S WRITE A NEWSPAPER STORY

Famous penguins are always appearing in the pages of the newspaper. Whether it's Gary the Gadget Guy being interviewed about his latest invention or an exclusive article with the penguins who first discovered the Forest and Cove, you'll find it in *The Club Penguin Times*. Practise your interviewing skills while pretending to be the island's most legendary penguin– Captain Rockhopper himself! Answer the questions opposite as though you were Rockhopper. If you need some help, see *How to Talk Like a Pirate* below. You can also visit the Book Room in the Coffee Shop and read the *Journal of Captain Rockhopper* to get a feel for the pirate penguin.

HOW TO TALK LIKE A PIRATE

Shiver me timbers! So ye want to talk like a pirate, do ye? Talking like a pirate is as easy as replacing "my" or "mine" with "me," and "you" with "ye" and using some pirate phrases such as:

Ahoy = Hello
Avast = Stop; Who goes there?
Aye = Yes
Doubloon = Spanish gold coin
Fair winds = Goodbye; Good luck

Gangway = Get out of the way
Landlubber = A non-sailor
Me hearty = My friend
Sail ho! = I see a ship
Shiver me timbers = An expression of surprise

Smartly = Quickly

HERE ARE SOME EXAMPLES:

Ahoy, me hearty!

Smartly now, let's count up me doubloons and set sail for the open seas.

Shiver me timbers!

What's this landlubber doing on me ship?

ROCKHOPPER INTERVIEW

Where can penguins find you when you visit Club Penguin?

Rockhopper:_____

What's your favourite Club Penguin game?

Rockhopper:_____

Who is your best friend?

Rockhopper:_____

Is it true that you discovered red puffles?

Rockhopper:_____

How much treasure do you have?

Rockhopper:_____

What is your most valued possession?

Rockhopper:_____

When are you coming back to Club Penguin?

Rockhopper:_____

JUST JOKING!

Penguins love to laugh. Waddle around the island and you'll see plenty of penguins telling jokes. Or pick up the latest edition of *The Club Penguin Times*. In each issue you'll find reader-submitted jokes. Here are some favourites:

Where do penguins go to dance?
The snow ball!

Why is it so easy to weigh fish?
They have their own scales!

What do penguins eat for lunch?
Ice burg-ers!

Why did the cookie go to the doctor?
It felt crummy!

Where do penguins keep their money?
In a snowbank!

What did the teddy bear say when he was offered dessert?
"No, thanks, I'm stuffed!"

What did the penguin eat for breakfast?
Snowflakes!

How do you cut the sea in half?
With a sea-saw!

How does a penguin make pancakes?
With its flippers!

Why can't you tell an egg a joke?
Because it will crack up!

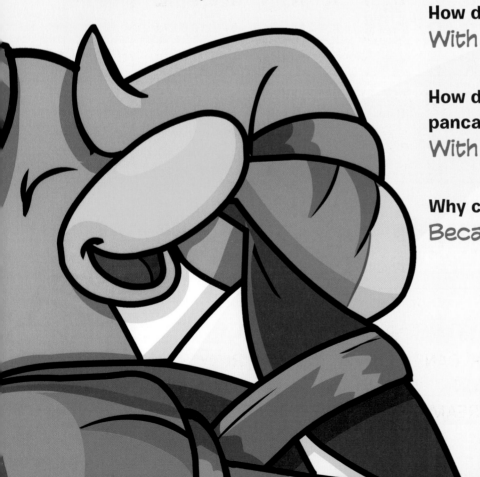

HIDDEN PINS WORDSEARCH

Every two weeks, a new pin is hidden for you to find, collect, and proudly display on your player card. You'll find a notice in *The Club Penguin Times* when a new pin is hidden. Put your pin-hunting skills to the test right now. See if you can find the names of previously hidden pins in this wordsearch puzzle.

```
W C Q U F O L F E D B I T C O
N I T H A V Y T Q X W E R V T
D V L O F P E A V A E A H O I
C K O S R X K V F F Y A M I W
H E L E V O H S W O N S C B J
A N L Y Y X Q L N V P E A E E
C A I G B C R B I O C S T M L
A C P P H U L L T R K T R I L
N Y O M W D R O E E Y M U T Y
C D P R Y K F A T F I S X O F
H N P J O G M B Y L U N Z P I
O A S Q O C A S C T Q B D H S
R C D L O L H D C B F O J A H
J J D N L V P A P F X V W T R
N N E J F W C F T E F C V O G
```

WORD BANK:

ANCHOR	CANDY CANE	JELLYFISH	RUBY
ANVIL	CRAYON	KEY	SNOW SHOVEL
BASKETBALL	ICE CREAM	LOLLIPOP	TOP HAT
CACTUS	CONE	POT OF GOLD	UFO

PENGUIN POETS

Roses are red and penguins are green, peach, black, red, yellow, brown, pink, orange and blue! Penguins are also very talented poets. Maybe you've read some of your fellow penguins' poems in *The Club Penguin Times*. Have you ever wanted to write your own poem? In this section, you'll learn how to write haikus - a really fun kind of poem to write. You can submit them to Aunt Arctic at the Club Penguin Times!

HAIKU

Haiku is a form of Japanese poetry-and it happens to be Sensei's favourite kind. Most haiku poems have three short lines. The first and last lines of a haiku have five syllables; the middle line has seven. Not sure what a syllable is? Syllables are the number of sounds, or beats, in each word. For example, *penguin* has two syllables: pen-guin. *Rockhopper* has three syllables: Rock-hop-per. One of the best things about a haiku is that it doesn't need to rhyme. Since haikus are so short, it's best to pick one thing to write about. Here are some examples:

A New Puffle
Inside the Pet Shop.
Puffles, puffles everywhere.
How do I decide?

Ice Fishing
Ice Fishing is cool.
The fish gobble up my worms.
Oops, I caught a crab.

The Pizza Parlor
The pizza is great.
I like it with fish and squid,
Sometimes with candy.

Give it a try! Write your own haikus below. They can be about a snowball fight, a fun party, or your favourite place or penguin on the island. Use your imagination!

RIDDLE ME THIS

What's full of holes but still holds water?

A SPONGE

AWESOME ANAGRAMS

An anagram is what you get when you take one word and rearrange the letters to form one or more new words from it. For example, using the letters in *snow*, you can make the word *owns*.

Here are ten anagrams made from the names of penguins, places, and things on Club Penguin. Rearrange the letters in the words to spell out each of the words in the Word Bank.

1 Sleepy Tuning _____

2 Inch Tie _____

3 Sees In _____

4 Meet So _____

5 Wall Snob _____

6 Bid Dues _____

7 Icons _____

8 Laced Grins _____

9 Posh Ports _____

10 Height Soul _____

WORD BANK:

BUDDIES

COINS

EMOTES

LIGHTHOUSE

PENGUIN STYLE

SENSEI

SLED RACING

SNOWBALL

SPORT SHOP

THIN ICE

RIDDLE ME THIS

What is there more of the less you see?

DARKNESS

PUT YOUR MEMORY TO THE TEST

Study this picture of the Town Center carefully. Then turn the page and see how many questions you can answer correctly without peeking!

MEMORY TEST: YOUR ANSWERS

1 How many puffles are there?

_____

2 What colour puffle is the red penguin holding?

_____

3 Who is peeking out behind the Coffee Shop sign?

_____

4 How many penguins are pictured?

_____

5 What does the sign say that the dark blue penguin is holding up?

_____

6 Are there any pink penguins in this picture?

_____

7 How many tables are in front of the Coffee Shop?

_____

8 One of the penguins is wearing a costume. What is it?

_____

9 What colour is the penguin flying with the jet pack?

_____

10 Are any of the puffles pink?

_____

PUFFLE RESCUE

Oh no! One of Aunt Arctic's beloved pet puffles is lost. Can you lead Aunt Arctic through the maze and reunite her with her puffle?

NAME THAT CHARACTER

ACROSS

1. This three-eyed alien is a crew member of the SS *Astro-Barrier*.
4. She's a daring treasure hunter who travels the world in search of rare puffles.
7. This defender of Club Penguin defeats villains with his Shadow Wave.
8. He uttered the famous lines, "To fish or not to fish; that is the question."

DOWN

1. He's the moose mascot for the Blue Team.
2. A pink powerhouse who packs a punch – watch out for her Gamma Wave.
3. He's a curious penguin who wanted to travel back in time.
5. When this penguin lost her precious gem, she had to ask Detective Jacque Hammer for help.
6. She's a fairy storyteller who lives in a magical library.

THE PIZZA PARLOR PUZZLE

Something is wrong with the Pizza Parlor's menu. All of the pizza names are scrambled! Help out the hungry customers by rearranging the letters to find the name of a delicious penguin pizza. If you're really stuck, use the word bank at the bottom of the page.

MIRSHP PIZZA _____

YELLJ NEAB PIZZA _____

CIPYS QUIDS PIZZA _____

COCOLATEH PERSLINK PIZZA _____

SHIF HSID PIZZA _____

KNIP ASURG PIZZA _____

AWESEED IFSH PIZZA _____

CIRCEOIL PICH PIZZA _____

WORD BANK:

CHOCOLATE SPRINKLE	JELLY BEAN	PINK SUGAR	SHRIMP
FISH DISH	LICORICE CHIP	SEAWEED FISH	SPICY SQUID

HOW TO DRAW A PENGUIN

Have you ever wondered how to draw a penguin? You can learn with these tips that will teach you how to draw your very own penguin. Grab a pencil and rubber for this activity so you can easily fix any mistakes.

STEP 1

A piece of art must begin simply, and this penguin you are about to draw is no different! First, draw two circles like a snowman – a big circle on the bottom and a smaller one on top for his head. Then connect the two circles you made, just like in the example below.

STEP 2

No penguin is complete without eyes and a beak! To help you see where they should be, draw a line lightly down the centre of the shape you made. Then draw another line from left to right across the penguin's head. Now, it's time to place the eyes and the beak. The eyes are two squashed circles pressed together. The beak should be placed right below the eyes. The beak is a squashed circle, too. Don't forget to give your penguin a smile!

STEP 3

Create your penguin's feet by making two triangles underneath the bottom of the egg shape. Think of it like drawing two slices of pizza. But instead of your triangles having sharp corners, round them out, so they don't look too pointy. Then add the lines inside, just like in the picture.

STEP 4

Start drawing your penguin's arms just under the bottom of the beak. To make sure you place the arms correctly, lightly draw a dotted line going from left to right underneath the beak. To make the arms, start at the dotted line you drew, and on either side of your penguin, just make two lines coming down to a point, like a very long triangle, just like in the picture below.

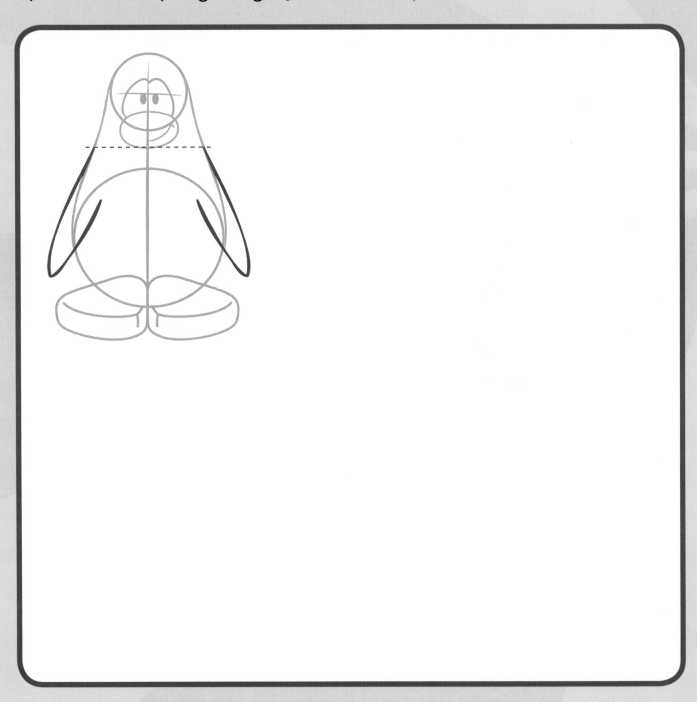

STEP 5

Your penguin is almost done. Up until now, you have drawn guidelines. Artists use guidelines to make sure the drawing will be done correctly. On top of your guidelines, you want to make detail lines. Detail lines are the final step, and are drawn much darker than the guidelines. Draw an outline around the body, arms, eyes, beak, feet, and smile. (And give your penguin dots inside its eyes so it can see!) Oh, and don't forget the tummy patch! A penguin just isn't a penguin without a white tummy. You just drew your own penguin!

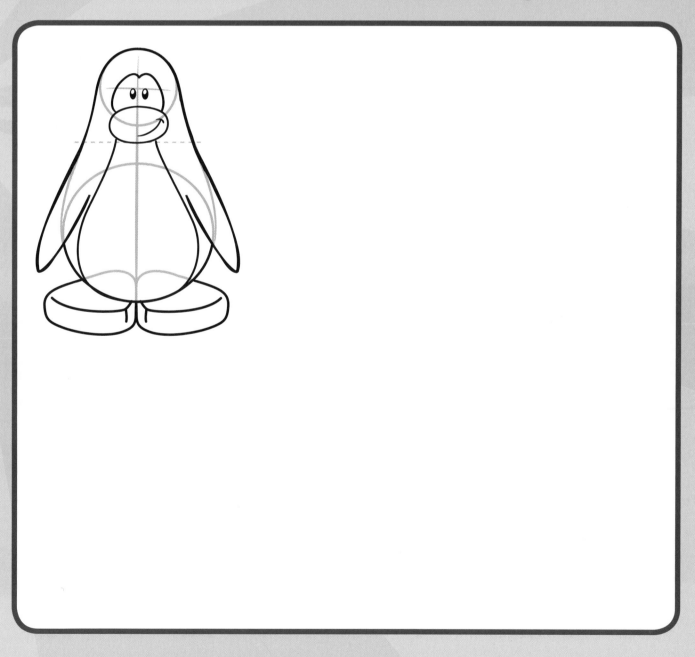

HOW TO DRAW A PUFFLE

You've learned how to draw penguins. Now it's time your penguin had a friend. What better friend for a penguin to have than a puffle?

STEP 1

Start by drawing a small circle – don't worry, it doesn't have to be a perfect circle. Next, lightly draw a line down the side of the circle. This line shows you where your puffle will be facing, and where you will soon place his eyes and smile! Then draw another line from left to right across the middle of the circle.

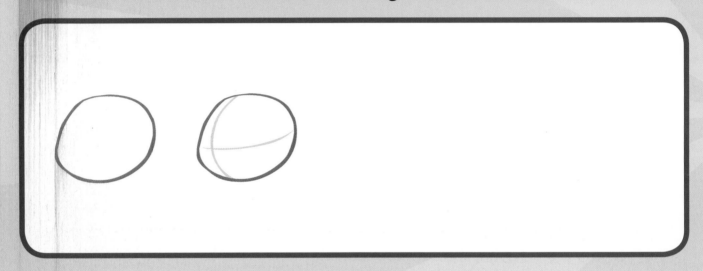

STEP 2

Puffles need to see! The puffle's eyes are a lot like how we drew the penguin's eyes earlier - like two squashed circles. But now, draw them a little bigger than how they were drawn before.

STEP 3

Underneath the eyes, but slightly to the right will be your puffle's mouth. Just draw two lines that are on top of each other in a smiling shape, and connect them to a point at the corner of the mouth. Then connect them with a line at the front of the mouth to show that your puffle has teeth. You can even add some detail to the teeth, like in the picture below.

STEP 4

To give your puffle hair, begin at the top of the circle, and draw a zigzag line floating slightly above the circle. Just like before, all of those lines you just drew were guidelines. Now, just like when you finished up your penguin, go over the important lines with a dark pencil or marker . . . and your puffle is complete!

SPOT THE DIFFERENCES

Do you want to walk the path of the ninja? Seek wisdom by comparing the two pictures of the mysterious and ancient Dojo. Fifteen things have been changed in the picture on the bottom. See if you can spot and circle all the differences.

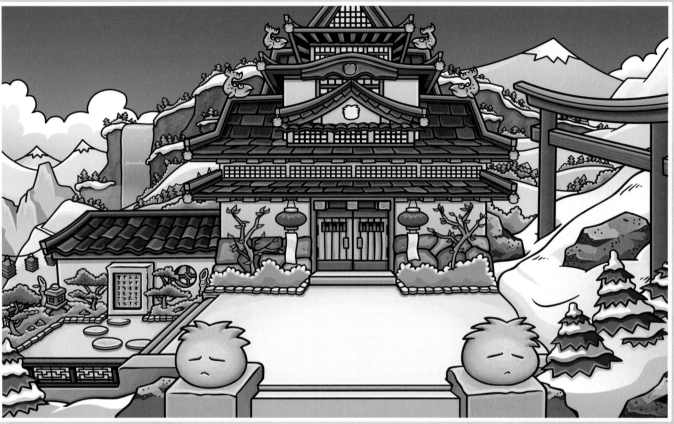

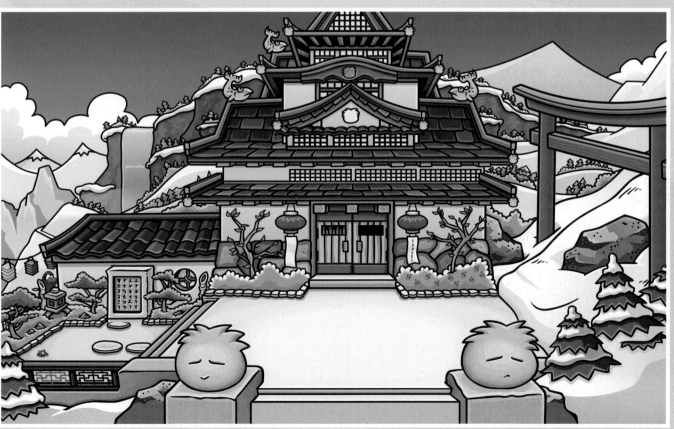

CARD-JITSU

Many years ago, Sensei built the Dojo to train ninjas. To become a ninja, you must play Card-Jitsu.

How to Play

1. Each turn, both pupils pick a card to play. Secret. Quiet. Like ninja.

2. The white icy snow brings with it the winter's chill, and freezes water.

3. Furious fire brings its might, scorching heat, and will melt the snow.

4. When cards are the same, the match is not yet over. Highest number wins.

Much like the Forest, there are two paths you can walk to reach victory.
The first way to win:
Have three cards of the same type in different colours.
The second path is:
To have one of each card type in different colours.
After winning many Card-Jitsu battles, pupils receive belt.

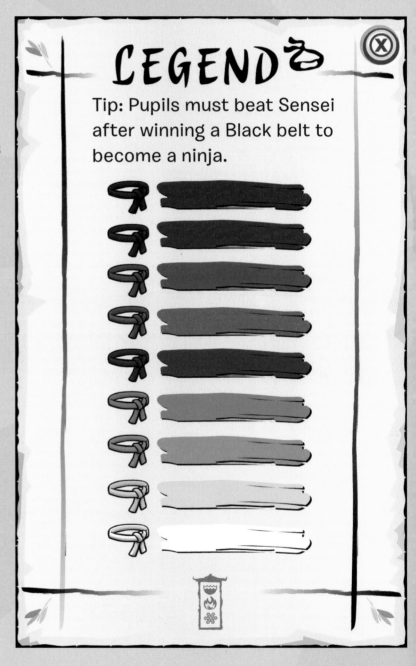

LEGEND

Tip: Pupils must beat Sensei after winning a Black belt to become a ninja.

 beats beats beats

BLACK BELT PANCAKES

These sensei-tional Black Belt Pancakes will hit the spot!

Prep Time: 10 min.
Cook Time: 15 min.
Ready in: 25 min.
Yield: 4-6 servings

Ingredients

125g flour

1 egg

3 tablespoons white sugar

300ml semi-skimmed milk

1 teaspoon baking powder

4 tablespoons vegetable oil

1 teaspoon bicarbonate of soda

¼ teaspoon salt

milk chocolate chips

Directions

We recommend having a more experienced master of the kitchen (a parent or guardian) help you with the instructions below.

1   Fire Card - Preheat a frying pan to medium heat. While it warms, gather these items: a blender; scales, measuring spoons, and a pancake flipper.

2   Water Card - Measure all the ingredients carefully and mix them (except for the chocolate chips) together in a blender.

3   Fire Card - Pour batter into the frying pan in the shape of a penguin. When bubbles stop appearing on top, use your pancake flipper to flip it over. Cook until pancake is bamboo-mat brown (commonly known as golden brown), then remove it from the pan.

4   Winner! - Now it's time to award your newly grilled ninja a black belt! Do this by making a line of milk chocolate chips across its waist. Once your pancakes have cooled enough to eat, add your favourite toppings and dig in! Finally, be sure to share this recipe with family, friends, and fellow ninjas!

PENGUIN, PLACE OR THING?

Can You Guess Who (or What) I Am?

1 You'll never find me in the same place twice in a row.

2 I am very popular. You'll always find a lot of penguins around me.

3 I always look different.

4 Searching for me is a fun game that many penguins enjoy.

5 If you want to know if it is time to start looking for me, check *The Club Penguin Times*.

6 I never hide in the Town Center.

7 Once you find me, I'm yours to keep.

8 I have been an anchor, teddy bear, balloon, taco, musical note, and even a box of Puffle-Os.

Do you know who or what I am?
_____

PENGUINS AT WORK LOGIC PUZZLE

These four penguins are about to start their new jobs. Can you figure out which penguin is doing which job? Carefully read the clues below to find out!

1 The black penguin's job requires a rake.

2 The pink penguin and the red penguin both have jobs that can save someone's life.

3 The red penguin needs to know how to swim for its job.

	CHEF	FIREFIGHTER	GARDENER	LIFEGUARD
RED PENGUIN				
PINK PENGUIN				
BLACK PENGUIN				
PURPLE PENGUIN				

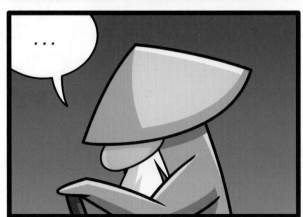

DESIGN YOUR OWN CATALOGUE

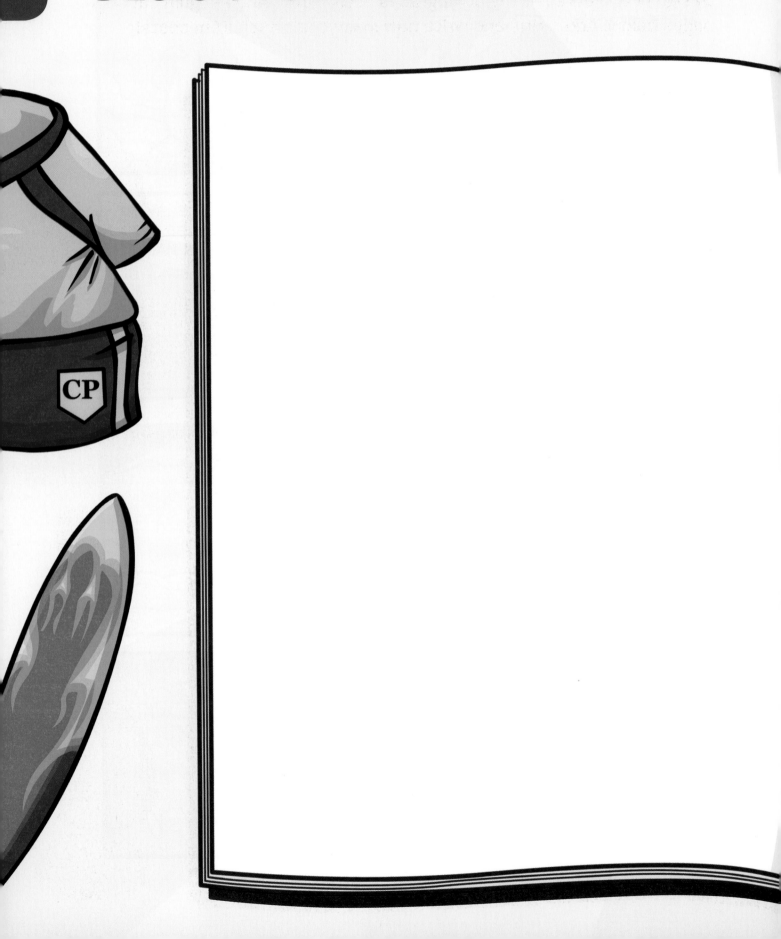

WHAT TO PUT IN IT

Design cool clothes and igloo upgrades in your own Club Penguin catalogue pages below. Add a title and write how many coins each item costs!

PENGUIN BAND PUZZLE

The Penguin Band is going to put on a surprise concert on the island. To find out where the band will play, follow the instructions below to cross out letters in the grid. The remaining letters will spell out the name of the place where you can catch the show!

1 Cross out any letters found in this penguin's name.

2 Do you know who this puffle is?

Here's a hint: He's the first mate of the Migrator.
Cross out any letters found in his name.

3 Cross out any letters that appear in this place's name.

4 Cross out any letters left in column 2.

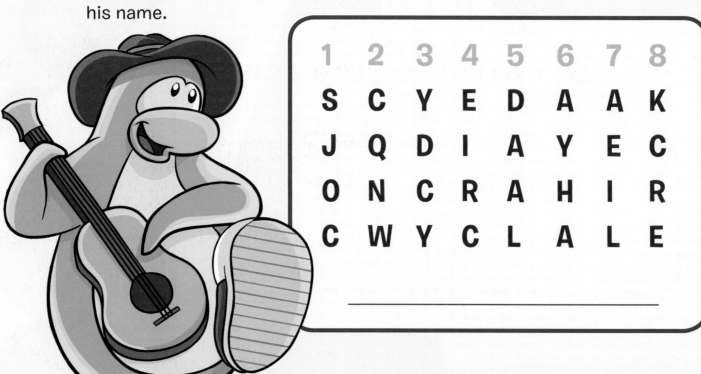

	1	2	3	4	5	6	7	8
	S	C	Y	E	D	A	A	K
	J	Q	D	I	A	Y	E	C
	O	N	C	R	A	H	I	R
	C	W	Y	C	L	A	L	E

_____

PENGUIN, PLACE OR THING?

Can You Guess Who (or What) I Am?

1 I am bright and colourful.

2 I am always moving, but I stay in one spot.

3 I am very loud.

4 I can help you test your skills against other penguins.

5 You can mix it up when you visit me.

6 I love to party.

7 Purple puffles love to visit me, but you'll always find a green puffle with me.

8 You can find me in the Town Center.

Do you know who or what I am?

MAP IT OUT

Many penguins use this map to get around Club Penguin. Put your knowledge of the island to the test by following these instructions.

1 Put an X on top of the building that has a secret entrance to the Boiler Room.

2 Circle the place where you can play *Catchin' Waves*.

3 Draw a puffle next to the place where the first yellow puffle was spotted.

4 Draw a triangle over the place where waiters and chefs work.

5 Write a *W* next to the place where you can find a waterfall.

6 Draw a square above the place that you need to avoid sharks, icebergs, seagulls, and floating logs, while playing the mini-game there.

7 Write a *T* next to the place where you can find the Tours Booth.

8 Put a star over the place where you can play a mini-game with your pink puffle.

9 Write an *R* next to the place where you can find the *Migrator* when it comes to Club Penguin.

10 Draw a snowflake next to the place where you can sledge or toboggan downhill.

PUFFLE SHUFFLE

Puffles make fantastic pets, but they have very different characters. How well do you know all your puffle personalities? Draw a line to match each cute puffball to its personality trait.

1

2

3

4

5

6

7

8

9

a) Adventurous and enthusiastic

b) Strong, silent type

c) Energetic and playful

d) Mild-tempered, content, loyal

e) A bit of a diva and a picky eater

f) Active and cheery

g) Artistic and spontaneous

h) Zany and curious

i) Gentle, strong

ICE MAZE

Your pet puffle is lost! Find the right path through the icy maze to rescue him. He'll be getting hungry, so see how many Puffle O's you can collect on the way, but make sure you don't fall down any snow holes!

Start!

Finish!

NAME THAT GAME

ACROSS

5. A smart grasshopper can earn a black belt.
7. Hold on tight and look for life preservers.
8. Watch out for sharks but try to snag the mullet.
10. Capture the most stones to win.
12. Soar through the sky in this game.
14. Explore the ocean depths and search for treasure.
16. A firey black puffle leads the way.
17. You can only play this game when Rockhopper is visiting the island.

DOWN

1. Challenge your buddies to a snowy chase.
2. The perfect game for bookworms.
3. Catch as many puffles as you can in the shortest amount of time.
4. Perform totally tubular tricks for more coins.
6. Avoid anvils, fish, and flowerpots.
9. Make mine a hot shrimp squid.
11. Go solo or boogie with the best.
13. Take a wild underground ride.
15. Strategy, not speed, is the key to this game.

PUFFLE ROUNDUP WORDSEARCH

Uh-oh! The puffles have escaped from the Pet Shop. It's your job to locate the puffles and their favourite toys and herd them back into their pen. To catch them, find and circle their names and toys in this wordsearch. Remember to search backward, forward, and diagonally.

```
P P W D V K G L C C P I N K R
J J U U N I C Y C L E V I V P
N D Y R O D I S C O B A L L E
V O E F P A I N T B R U S H Y
I Z N R T L B W H S X O G B S
M Y R N O H E A O Z T C F R K
S I D R A O B E T A K S M C C
L L Y T W C J E T I H W Y N A
P R K E R X R M D E T A K S L
S T J G L U R M Y P D G R N B
T U Y X R L D F B A S G K G A
U H E N I L O P M A R T M W L
R W W U E A E W C E J M F S L
C T U O L T K K E L R D R F U
F L P M V B R N H H O P Y K Z
```

WORD BANK:

BALL	DISCO BALL	PURPLE	TRAMPOLINE
BLACK	GREEN	RED	UNICYCLE
BLUE	PAINTBRUSH	SKATE	WHITE
CANNON	PINK	SKATEBOARD	YELLOW

PICK THE PUFFLE

Cadence, Rockhopper, Aunt Arctic, Sensei, and Gary the Gadget Guy are all at the Pet Shop looking for new pet puffles. They ended up choosing a white puffle, a black puffle, a purple puffle, a yellow puffle and a pink puffle. To figure out who chose which puffle, read the following clues.

A Gary's puffle knows how to skateboard.

B Cadence chose a puffle that loves to dance.

C The puffle that Sensei chose was spotted for the first time in the Dojo courtyard.

D Rockhopper's puffle's favourite game is *Aqua Grabber*.

E The puffle that Aunt Arctic chose loves to play with an easel and paintbrush.

CAN YOU GUESS WHAT PUFFLE THE PENGUINS CHOSE?

1 Cadence picked the _____ puffle.

2 Rockhopper picked the _____ puffle.

3 Aunt Arctic picked the _____ puffle.

4 Gary picked the _____ puffle.

5 Sensei picked the _____ puffle.

FIND THE HIDDEN ITEM

Penguins always love searching for hidden items in the Penguin Style catalogue. Imagine that a new Penguin Style is out and three items are hidden inside the catalogue: the Viking helmet, the Spikester and one other item. To find out what it is, follow the instructions below to cross out letters in the grid. The remaining letters will spell out the name of the final item hidden in the Penguin Style catalogue.

1 Cross out any letters found in this penguin's name.

3 Cross out any letters that appear in this creature's name.

4 Cross out the letters in the initials that the secret agents call this place.

2 Cross out any letters in the name of this place.

5 Cross out any letters left in column 7.

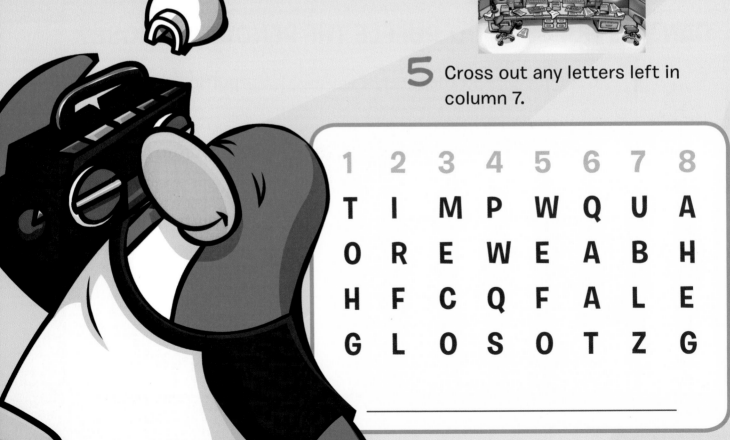

1	2	3	4	5	6	7	8
T	I	M	P	W	Q	U	A
O	R	E	W	E	A	B	H
H	F	C	Q	F	A	L	E
G	L	O	S	O	T	Z	G

_____

SPORTY PENGUINS LOGIC PUZZLE

These six penguins are about to play their favourite sports. Can you figure out which penguin is playing which sport? Carefully read the clues below to find out!

1 The yellow penguin plays a sport that requires a racket.

2 The red penguin plays a sport with a ball, and so does the blue penguin.

3 The green penguin and black penguin both play their sports in the water.

4 The red penguin doesn't use a bat to play his sport.

5 The black penguin uses a special board to play her sport.

	BASEBALL	TENNIS	ROCK CLIMBING	FOOTBALL	SURFING	SWIMMING
YELLOW PENGUIN						
RED PENGUIN						
GREEN PENGUIN						
PINK PENGUIN						
BLACK PENGUIN						
BLUE PENGUIN						

WELL, HEY! GOOD TO SEE YOU ALL.

WHY DON'T WE START WITH YOU GUYS SHOWING ME YOUR MOVES?

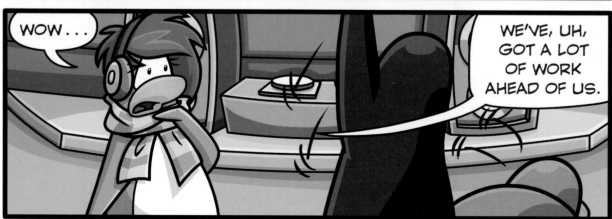

WOW . . .

WE'VE, UH, GOT A LOT OF WORK AHEAD OF US.

PENGUIN PLAY AWARDS PARTY
How It's Done

- Make sure your parent or guardian helps you with these!

- Plan your own party!

- Get your parent or guardian's permission and make the invitations on the next page.

- Check out these ideas for an awesome Penguin Play Awards Party!

1 Dress up!

2 Pretend you're the paparazzi and take lots of photos.

3 Make silver stars with each guest's name on them to decorate your room.

4 Vote on your favourite TV shows or choose between 5 DVDs to watch.

5 Interview your guests about each show.

6 Give out awards to your guests in categories like best dressed, funniest and friendliest.

7 Serve Stage Snacks! You can find these on the Club Penguin website by going to the Community section and going to Fun Activities: community.clubpenguin.com/funactivities/

8 Makeover your guests with face paints and fun accessories.

9 Give a speech thanking everyone for coming.

10 Put together a scrapbook of your evening.

● Ask your parent or guardian to help you photocopy this page - one for each guest. Colour it in, fill in the details, then carefully cut it out. Fold the long dotted line first, then the shorter one, so that the Penguin Play Award is the cover of your invitation.

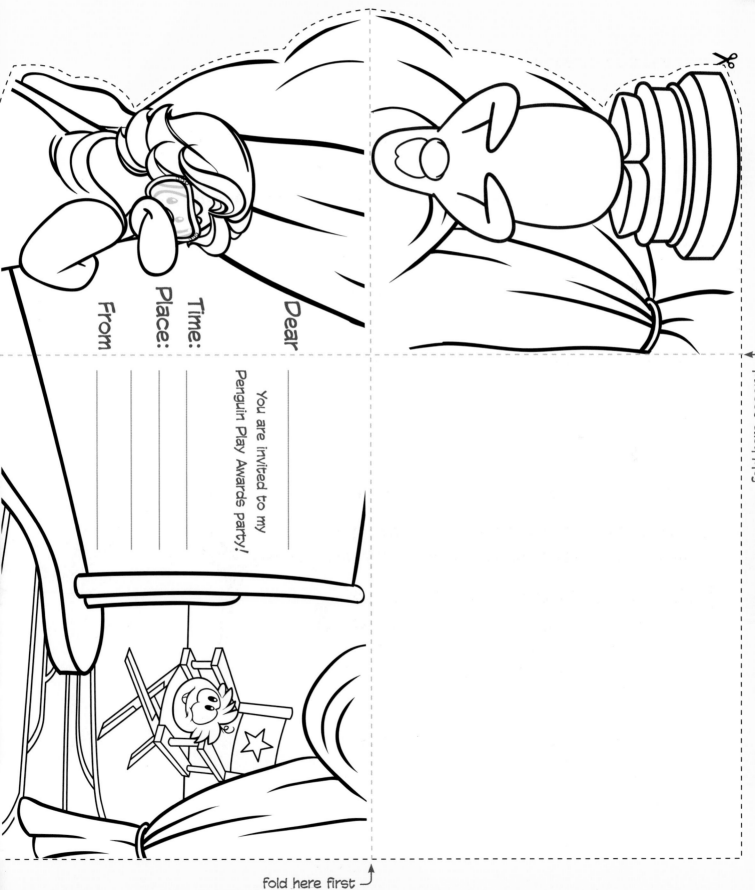

Dear _____

You are invited to my Penguin Play Awards party!

Time: _____

Place: _____

From _____

fold here second

fold here first

SPOT THE DIFFERENCES

Can you help Shadow Guy and Gamma Gal save the day by spotting the differences? Look carefully at the two pictures to the right. Fifteen things have been changed in the picture on the bottom. See if you can spot and circle all of the differences.

PENGUIN POWER!

Create your very own super penguin! Imagine it has special powers - maybe it can fly or change shape, see through walls or see the answers to the activities in this book. Draw a picture of it below.

ANSWER KEY

Page 8
ROCKHOPPER'S TREASURE HUNT

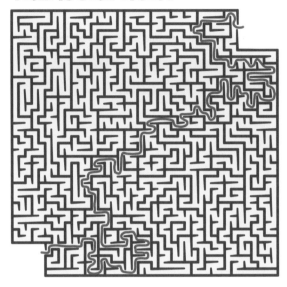

Page 9
PENGUIN, PLACE OR THING?

Aye, mateys! You guessed it. It's me, Rockhopper! I'm always on the hunt for treasure while sailing the seas on me ship, the *Migrator*, with me first mate, Yarr.

Pages 13
HIDDEN PINS WORDSEARCH

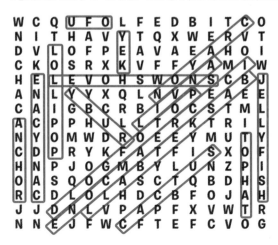

Page 16
AWESOME ANAGRAMS

1. Penguin Style
2. Thin Ice
3. Sensei
4. Emotes
5. Snowball
6. Buddies
7. Coins
8. Sled Racing
9. Sport Shop
10. Lighthouse

Pages 17-18
PUT YOUR MEMORY TO THE TEST

1. three
2. blue
3. a secret agent
4. nine
5. tours
6. no
7. two
8. a fish costume
9. orange
10. yes

Page 19
PUFFLE RESCUE

ANSWER KEY

Page 22
NAME THAT CHARACTER

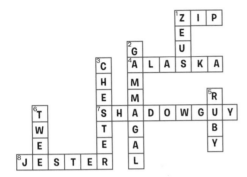

Page 23
THE PIZZA PARLOR PUZZLE

Shrimp pizza
Jelly bean pizza
Spicy squid pizza
Chocolate sprinkle pizza
Fish dish pizza
Pink sugar pizza
Seaweed fish pizza
Licorice chip pizza

Page 30-31
SPOT THE DIFFERENCES

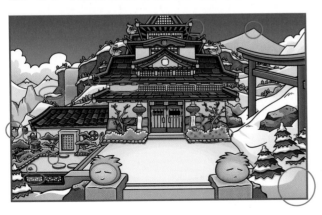

Page 34
PENGUIN, PLACE OR THING?

I am a pin! Every two weeks, a new pin is hidden on Club Penguin.
A pin is a small picture that you can add to your player card.

Page 35
PENGUINS AT WORK LOGIC PUZZLE

Red penguin=Lifeguard
Pink penguin=Firefighter
Black penguin=Gardener
Purple penguin=Chef

Page 40
PENGUIN BAND PUZZLE

Ski Hill

Page 41
PENGUIN, PLACE OR THING?

I am the Night Club! Penguins flock to my brightly lit dance floor to practice the latest dance moves.

ANSWER KEY

Pages 42-43
MAP IT OUT

1. Night Club; 2. Cove; 3. Forest; 4. Pizza Parlor; 5. Dojo; 6. Dock; 7. Ski Village; 8. Iceberg; 9. Beach; 10. Ski Hill.

Page 44
PUFFLE SHUFFLE

1. d   8. i
2. a   9. g
3. f
4. b
5. c
6. h
7. e

Page 45
ICE MAZE

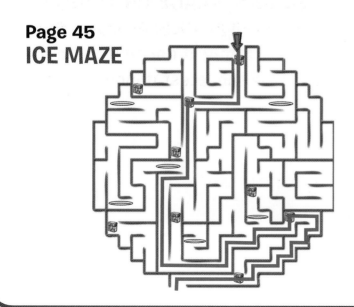

Page 46-47
NAME THAT GAME

Page 48
PUFFLE ROUNDUP WORDSEARCH

P P W D V K G L C C P I N K R
J J U U N I C Y C L E V I V P
N D Y R O D I S C O B A L L E
V O E F P A I N T B R U S H Y
I Z N R T L B W H S X O G B S
M Y R N O H E A O Z T C F R K
S I L D R A O B E T A K S M C
L I R Y T W C J E T I H W Y N
P R K E R X R M D E T A K S A
S T J G L U R M Y P D G R L B
T U Y X R L D F B A S G K N A
U H E N I L O P M A R T M W L
R W W U E A E W C E J M F S L
C T U O L T K K E L R D R Y U
F L P M V B R N H H O P Y K Z

Page 49
PICK THE PUFFLE

1. purple
2. pink
3. yellow
4. black
5. white

ANSWER KEY

Page 50
FIND THE HIDDEN ITEM
Maracas

Page 51
SPORTY PENGUINS LOGIC PUZZLE
The yellow penguin plays tennis; the red penguin plays football; the green penguin swims; the pink penguin rock climbs; the black penguin surfs; and the blue penguin plays baseball.

Pages 56–57
SPOT THE DIFFERENCES

COLLECT THESE OTHER GREAT CLUB PENGUIN TITLES!

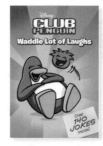